LIVING
ON THE EDGE

BIBLE STUDY

Overcoming Emotions That Destroy

Practical Help for Those Angry Feelings That Ruin Relationships

Chip Ingram

Overcoming Emotions That Destroy

Table of Contents

Small Group

The fact that you are even reading this page says a lot about you. It says that you are either one of those people that has to read everything, or you are at least open to being used by God to lead a group.

Leading a small group can sound intimidating, but it really doesn't have to be. Think of it more as gathering a few friends to get to know each other better and to have some discussion around spiritual matters.

Here are a few practical tips to help you get started:

1. Pray

One of the most important principles of spiritual leadership is to realize you can't do this on your own. No matter how long we've been leading, we need the power of the Holy Spirit. Lean on Him… He will help you.

2. Invite some friends

Don't be afraid to ask people to come to your group. You will be surprised how many people are open to such a study, especially when you let them know that the study is only for 8 weeks. Whether you have 4 or 14 in your group, it can be a powerful experience. You should probably plan on at least an hour and a half for your group meeting.

3. Get your materials

You will need to get a DVD or use your streaming code for the video teaching done by Chip Ingram. You can get the DVD from LivingontheEdge.org Also, it will be helpful for each person to have their own study guide. You can also purchase those through the website.

4. Be prepared to facilitate

Just a few minutes a week in preparation can make a huge difference in the group experience. Each week preview the video teaching and review the discussion questions. If you don't think your group can get through all the questions, select the ones that are most relevant to your group.

5. Love your group

Maybe the most important thing you bring to the group is your personal care for them. If you will pray for them, encourage them, call them, email them, involve them, and love them, God will be pleased and you will have a lot of fun along the way.

◢ LIVING ON THE EDGE™

FREE ACCESS TO VIDEO TEACHING

You can stream it for FREE by following the directions below.
Or you can order a DVD at (888) 333-6003 or
LivingontheEdge.org.

YOUR ONLINE CODE

7442126-4VS8-MRM7

 Please visit LivingontheEdge.org/access and enter this code.

3 EASY STEPS

1 | **CREATE AN ACCOUNT**
Go to LivingontheEdge.org/access and complete
the steps to create your FREE account.

2 | **GET IMMEDIATE ACCESS**
Now you will be connected to the resources which
will be needed throughout this workbook.

3 | **ACCESS ANYTIME**
• Log back into your account anytime by visiting
LivingontheEdge.org and click on STORE.
• From the STORE page, click on Login/Register.
• Enter your login information. Once you are in your
account, click on MEMBERSHIPS.

Overcoming Emotions

Experience

You and your group are about to begin what could be a life-changing journey in your small group. This powerful study of Overcoming Emotions That Destroy provides some breakthrough teaching that will not only help your group discover their gifts but also learn how to develop and deploy them.

Listed below are the segments you will experience each week as well as some hints for getting the most out of this experience.

TAKE IT IN – WATCH THE VIDEO: During this section you will watch the video teaching. Each teaching segment is about 20 minutes long. A teaching outline with fill-ins is provided for each session. As you follow along, write down questions or insights that you can share during the discussion time. Also, bring your Bible each week.

TALK IT OVER: Several discussion questions are provided for your group to further engage the teaching content. Keep the following guidelines in mind for having a healthy group discussion.

- **Be involved.** Jump in and share your thoughts. Your ideas are important, and you have a perspective that is unique and can benefit the other group members.

- **Be a good listener.** Value what others are sharing. Seek to really understand the perspective of others in your group and don't be afraid to ask follow-up questions.

- **Be courteous.** Always treat others with utmost respect. When there is disagreement, focus on the issue and never turn the discussion into a personal attack.

- **Be focused.** Stay on topic. Help the group explore the subject at hand, and try to save unrelated questions or stories for afterwards.

- **Be careful not to dominate.** Be aware of the amount of talking you are doing in proportion to the rest of the group, and make space for others to speak.

- **Be a learner.** Stay sensitive to what God might be wanting to teach you through the lesson, as well as through what others have to say.

LIVE IT OUT: These simple suggestions help the lesson come to life. Don't ignore them; give them a try! Check in with another group member during the week and ask how it's going.

Overview

This teaching is available in audio, video, and book formats. The DVD resource is designed to have a personal study guide to accompany the DVD teaching. Each session corresponds to a specific section in the study guide to be used as a viewer's guide for taking notes during the DVD teaching. Talk It Over questions and Live It Out applications are available at the end of each session for personal reflection and/or group discussions.

For group studies, a "Leader's Notes" section can be found in the back of each study guide. This section contains tips for preparing and facilitating discussions. The session notes are brief highlights to aid in planning each week's sessions. Living on the Edge also has a "Coaching for Leaders" tab at our website www.LivingontheEdge.org, which through Q&A videos provides insight and support for small group facilitators.

The "Overcoming Emotions that Destroy" series is available in book form-which can be used as an enhancement to your study. It is NOT an additional tool but the same DVD teaching in a written format providing another source for supplementing your learning.

Free "Message Notes" are available for the audio formats–CD or MP3. Use the search icon on the home page www.LivingontheEdge.org and type "message notes." Scroll to find the message notes link; click and search by title. Message Notes are free and duplication is not under copyright restrictions.

Session 1

THE MONSTER THAT LIVES WITHIN

What has the Power to Destroy?

_____ – Designed as a gift from God, there are times, places and circumstances that bring out "emotions that destroy."

My dear brothers, take note of this: Everyone should be quick to listen, slow to speak and slow to become angry, for man's anger does not bring about the righteous life that God desires.　　　　**JAMES 1:19-20 NIV**

Warning: *Under Pressure we are all prone to "Blow a Fuse" or "Burn the House Down."*

ANGER TRIGGERS

- You feel categorized or stereotyped.
- You feel trapped.
- You were unfairly treated.
- You felt blamed.
- You feel ignored, misunderstood, insignificant, belittled, or put down.
- You felt entitled to something and didn't get it. Your expectations weren't met.
- You were given unsolicited advice, that someone has treated you in a condescending way.
- You were teased insensitively.
- You were criticized.
- You didn't feel that your limits were respected.
- You were given ultimatums or threats.
- You were kicked, pushed, slapped, or hit.
- Your space or territory has been invaded.
- You didn't feel safe.
- You feel self-pity.

A LOOK AT ANGER FROM GOD'S PERSPECTIVE

Definition: Anger is neither good nor bad; it is a "charged," morally neutral, emotional response of protective preservation.

- _____ – It can be a healthy emotion that motivates us to correct **attitudes**, **behaviors**, or **injustices** that we perceive to be wrong.

  "In your anger do not sin": Do not let the sun go down while you are still angry, and do not give the devil a foothold. EPHESIANS 4:26-27 NIV

- _____ – It can be an unhealthy and destructive emotional response to protect us from (real or perceived) **hurt**, **frustration**, or **personal attack**.

  A hot-tempered man must pay the penalty; if you rescue him, you will have to do it again. PROVERBS 19:19 NIV

  Do not make friends with a hot-tempered man; do not associate with one easily angered, PROVERBS 22:24 NIV

  An angry man stirs up dissension, and a hot-tempered one commits many sins. PROVERBS 29:22 NIV

QUESTIONS TO CONSIDER:

- Have you ever done something you wished you hadn't when you were angry?

- Have you ever said something you wish you could take back when you were angry?

- Have you ever made a bad decision when you were angry?

- Have you ever ruined a friendship, a marriage, a family relationship, or a ministry relationship because of anger?

- Have you ever seen a person hurt because of someone's anger—physically, emotionally, or psychologically?

SUMMARY:

Without exception, we all struggle with angry feelings at times; and those angry feelings have done more than their share of damage in our relationships with others.

 TALK IT OVER

1. When you were a kid, how did your parents' deal with anger in your home?

2. How do you sense that your parent's way of handling anger has impacted how you handle anger?

3. From the list of anger triggers, which 2 or 3 most resonate with your experience?

4. As you think about your normal week, what 1 or 2 events, circumstances, or situations can trigger anger in you?

5. Can you think of a time when you used your anger positively to stand up for an injustice?

6. When was a time that you saw anger used negatively and it caused hurt?

7. Spend a few minutes unpacking the practical meaning of Proverbs 19:19: "A hot-tempered man must pay the penalty; if you rescue him, you will have to do it again." What does Solomon mean when he says "if you rescue him, you will have to do it again"?

 LIVE IT OUT

Try to be more self-aware this week. Monitor your emotions. When is your anger most likely to be triggered?

Session 2

THE THREE FACES OF ANGER

We can be deceived regarding anger because…

we _____ our anger in such a wide variety of ways that many people assume _____ is **NOT** an issue in their life.

The heart is deceitful above all things and beyond cure. Who can understand it? "I the LORD search the heart and examine the mind, to reward a man according to his conduct, according to what his deeds deserve."

JEREMIAH 17:9-10 NIV

Mask #1 = The "_____"

Types: *Exploding time bombs (out of control) and calculated time bombs (in control)*

Message: *Anger is necessary.*

Reaction: *"You bet I'm mad!"; "Do what I say or else!"*

REASONS FOR EXPRESSING ANGER

- It can give them a false sense of power or control.
- It helps them to release pent-up negative emotions.
- They feel unable to constrain or control anger.

HOW THEY BLOW UP

- Yelling, screaming, shouting
- Pushing, shoving, hitting, kicking

- Intimidation
- Aggression
- By becoming overly opinionated
- By being overly blunt, forceful, or tactless
- By being demanding and repetitive

RESULTS

- Wound themselves and others
- Loss of control/power or a false sense of power
- Feelings of guilt
- Strained and unhealthy relationships
- Possible retaliation or revenge
- Possible damage and even violent behavior
- Regrets

WHAT SPEWERS (EXPLODERS AND CONTROLLERS) NEED

- To develop a longer fuse
- To learn to control anger
- To acknowledge their destructive expression and use of anger

A SPEWER SELF-ASSESSMENT

1. I can be blunt and forceful when someone does something to frustrate me.

2. As I speak my convictions my voice becomes increasingly louder.

3. When someone confronts me about a problem, I am likely to offer a ready rebuttal.

4. No one has to guess my opinion, I am known for having unwavering viewpoints.

5. When something goes wrong I focus so sharply on fixing the problem I often overlook people's feelings.

6. I have a history of getting caught in bickering matches with family members.

7. During verbal disagreements with someone I tend to repeat myself several times to make the point.

8. I find it hard to keep my thoughts to myself when I know something is wrong.

9. I have a reputation of being strong-willed.

10. I tend to give advice even when others have not asked for it.

Are you a spewer? ○ Yes ○ No ○ Maybe

Mask #2 = The "_____"

Types: *Repress (Deny/Avoid) or Suppress (Pretend/Stuff)*

Message: *Anger is bad.*

Reaction: *"Angry? Not me."*

WHY THEY ARE AFRAID OF ANGER:

- They think it's bad, even sinful, to be angry.
- They fear God's wrath.
- They fear loss of control and making a fool of themselves.
- They fear rejection (others won't like them if they get angry).
- They don't like to feel guilty.
- Their experience with anger was scary, so all anger is something to be avoided.

- They fear retaliation, punishment, or the consequences or the possible outcomes of expressing anger.

- Ignoring it

- Denying it

- Shielding/deflecting it

- Minimizing it

- Pretending they aren't really angry

- Avoiding it

- Burying it

RESULTS

- They become doormats (are taken advantage of).

- They redirect anger at themselves.

- They develop physical ailments: ulcers, muscle tension, headaches, etc.

- They occasionally erupt with volcanic-sized outbursts.

- They avoid people, places, and things.

- They develop resentments.

WHAT STUFFERS NEED

- To accept that anger is okay/normal

- To acknowledge fears and seek to minimize their hold on others

- To learn to communicate anger effectively

- To become more assertive with their needs and wants

- To become clearer about what they will and won't do

STUFFER SELF-ASSESSMENT

1. I am very image conscious, and I don't like to let others know my problems.

2. Even when I feel frustrated I portray myself publicly as having it all together.

3. I'm rather reserved about sharing my problems or my frustrations.

4. If a family member or friend upsets me I can let days pass without even mentioning it.

5. I have a tendency to be depressed and moody.

6. Resentful thinking is common for me although many people would never suspect it.

7. I've suffered with physical ailments… headaches, stomach ailments, and sleep irregularity.

8. There are times when I wonder if my opinions or preferences are really valid.

9. Sometimes I feel paralyzed when confronted by an unwanted situation.

10. I feel guilty a lot about little things, especially when someone is upset with me.

Are you a stuffer?　　　　　　　○ Yes　　○ No　　○ Maybe

Mask #3 = The "_____"

Types: *Indirect and Direct (Passive Aggressive)*

Message: *Showing anger is bad.*

Reaction: *"Angry? Not me. Well, maybe just a little."*

WHY THEY ARE AFRAID OF ANGER:

- They think it's bad, even sinful, to be angry.

- They fear God's wrath.

- They fear loss of control, "losing it," making a fool of themselves

- They fear rejection (others won't like them if they get angry).

- They don't like to feel guilty.

- Their experience with anger was scary, so all anger is something to be afraid of or avoided.

- They fear retaliation, punishment, or the consequences of expressing anger.

HOW THEY LEAK ANGER

- By not following through on commitments or promises.

- By not letting their "yes" be "yes" and their "no" be "no."

- By making excuses.

- By procrastinating.

- By knowingly going at a pace different than and annoying to others.

- By playing possum (or the helpless, ignorant victim role).

RESULTS

- They develop a false or unhealthy sense of power.

- They aggravate those around them and strain/weaken relationships.

- They become critical and negative.

- They become isolated.

- They become sarcastic.

- They are often late and they withdraw.

- They are often frigid sexually to pay back their mate.

- They forget and avoid issues.

WHAT LEAKERS NEED

- To accept that anger is okay/normal
- To acknowledge fears and seek to minimize their influence
- To learn to communicate anger effectively
- To become more assertive with their needs and wants
- To become clearer about what they will and won't do, and when

LEAKERS SELF-ASSESSMENT

1. When I am frustrated I become silent, knowing it bothers other people.

2. I am prone to sulk and pout.

3. When I don't want to do a project, I will procrastinate.

4. When someone asks me if I am frustrated I will lie and say, "No, everything is fine."

5. There are times when I am deliberately evasive so others won't bother me.

6. I sometimes approach work projects halfheartedly.

7. When someone talks to me about my problems I stare straight ahead being deliberately obstinate.

8. I am often sarcastic and hide my real hurts behind jokes.

9. I withdraw affection and become frigid when hurt.

10. I forget to do things for people when they have wounded me.

Are you a leaker?   ○ Yes   ○ No   ○ Maybe

💬 TALK IT OVER

1. What mask do you tend to wear? How did you learn to wear that mask?

   _____

   _____

2. In the one that is your primary expression (spewer, stuffer, or leaker)… which statement in the self-assessment do you most relate to? Which one least describes you?

   _____

   _____

3. In the one that is your primary expression (spewer, stuffer, or leaker)… which statement in the "What Spewers/Stuffers/Leakers Need" section do you need to work on?

   _____

   _____

4. What are some common things people say to "rationalize" or "defend" their anger?

   _____

   _____

5. When it comes to your anger, how can you be deceived?

   _____

   _____

6. Complete the following statement… "When people sense I am angry, the best way to respond is…."

   _____

   _____

⚙ LIVE IT OUT

Sit down with a friend this week and review the section that best describes you (spewer, leaker, or stuffer). Ask them for their insights and help with controlling your anger.

Session 3

ANGER IS A SECONDARY EMOTION
PART 1

Anger is like a red light on the dashboard of our car indicating that something under the hood is wrong.

- It's easier to be angry than face the _____.
- Anger is not the problem, it's the _____.

Anger _____ helps us feel in control when we are feeling out of control… and falsely helps us feel powerful when we feel powerless.

ANGER: THE TIP OF THE ICEBERG

1. _____ *comes from real or perceived unmet needs.*

A man's own folly ruins his life,
*   yet his heart rages against the LORD.*

PROVERBS 19:3 NIV

Anger is cruel and fury overwhelming,
*   but who can stand before jealousy?*

PROVERBS 27:4 NIV

BIBLICAL EXAMPLES:

- Joseph's brothers – unmet need by their father (Genesis 37-39)

but when his brothers saw that their father loved him more than all his brothers they hated him and could not speak peaceably to him.

GENESIS 37:4 NIV

- Lament Psalms (almost 25% of the Psalms are someone complaining to God)

TOOL #1 – HOW TO COMMUNICATE NEEDS:

- "I feel angry or hurt or disappointed when you _____."

⑪ TALK IT OVER

1. A few moments ago Chip asked God to bring to mind a situation where you have been hurt. If you are willing, share what/who came to mind. You don't have to share all the details but share a little about that experience. Then talk about how open you are to taking a step to sit down with this person and gently share with them "I feel hurt when…".

2. When trying to communicate an "I feel" message, what should you NOT do or say?

3. Think of something that makes you angry in your relationship with your spouse or good friend. How could you communicate that with an "I feel" message?

4. What are some of the unspoken expectations you have of the people around you that end up resulting in anger?

5. Can you think of a time recently when you got angry, but there was a deeper root issue causing the anger?

6. Chip said there are 3 big categories that drive our anger:
   1. Unmet needs (hurt)
   2. Unmet expectations (frustration)
   3. Insecurity

   Which one of these do you most struggle with? How does that play itself out in your life?

   _____

   _____

 **LIVE IT OUT**

Read Psalm 73. What are some insights we can learn from this passage when we feel angry because life has been unfair?

Session 4

ANGER IS A SECONDARY EMOTION
PART 2

2. _____ = *real or perceived*
   unmet expectations.

A patient man has great understanding,
*   but a quick-tempered man displays folly.*

PROVERBS 14:29 NIV

BIBLICAL EXAMPLES:

- Naaman (2 Kings 5:11-12)

  Anger is the distance between our experience and _____.

- Micah, David's Wife (1 Chronicles 15:29)

TOOL #2 – HOW TO COMMUNICATE FRUSTRATION:

- "I desire" vs. "I demand" expectations

  I desire _____

  I long for _____

  I hope for _____

  _____

  _____

3. _____ = *real or perceived*
attack on my personal worth

Anger is often _____ of insecurity in my life.

A gentle answer turns away wrath, but a harsh word stirs up anger.

PROVERBS 15:1 NIV

An offended brother is more unyielding than a fortified city, and disputes are like the barred gates of a citadel.

PROVERBS 18:19 NIV

Inadequacy produces fear rooted in shame. Inadequacy (insecurity) creates a fear of others seeing me as I am. So, I hide.

GENESIS 3

BIBLICAL EXAMPLES:

- Saul (1 Samuel 18:5-8)
- Jewish Leader (Acts 5:12-18)

TOOL #3 – ASK YOURSELF, "WHY AM I FEELING THREATENED?":

- What is being attacked?
- Who is attacking me?
- Is the threat menial or meaningful?
- Whose approval am I seeking?

The first step in overcoming the destructive power of anger is the_____ to look below the surface.

1. Talking about our insecurities is not easy. But naming them and identifying them will help raise our own self-awareness. So, as Chip challenged, share what triggers insecurity in you. Is there a recent experience where your insecurities were triggered?

2. Chip said, "Everybody is desperately insecure." And, he said that we have a tendency toward strong reaction (get defensive, power up) or a weak reaction (withdraw, isolate). What is your natural tendency?

3. How does having a strong identity in Christ help me with my insecurities? Read Ephesians 1:3-14. Which of these verses most speaks to you about your identity in Christ?

4. Chip said, "Inadequacy (insecurity) creates a fear of others seeing me as I am. So, I hide." How has this truth played itself out in your life?

5. For those of you who are married, what expectation did you have coming into your marriage that ended up causing conflict?

6. Do a little self-assessment. How much do you find yourself using the following words to communicate your expectations… "ought, should, always, never"?

7. Practice using the "I desire" vs. "I demand" tool. Take an expectation that you have had and turn it into a desire statement.

LIVE IT OUT

Spend some time this week reflecting on what Chip said about the insecurities that we each struggle with. Then, briefly write out your thoughts, starting with this sentence "I feel most insecure when…."

*Additional Resource: **Strong and the Weak** by Paul Tournier*

Session 5

HOW TO MAKE YOUR ANGER WORK FOR YOU

THE ABCD'S OF ANGER

- A – _____ (admit and accept) the anger

- B – _____ to the primary emotion

- C – _____ the cause

- D – _____ how best to deal with it

THE WHO, WHAT, HOW, AND WHEN OF DETERMINING HOW TO DEAL WITH ANGER

_____ **?**

- At whom am I really angry? Myself? Someone else? The situation? God?

_____ **?**

- What should I do? Express directly or release indirectly? (Confront or conceal?) Will my plans make matters worse or make them better?

_____ **?**

- How do I deal with the situation? In person? On the phone? Through a letter?

_____ **?**

- When should I deal with the situation? Now? Later? Never?

🕚 TALK IT OVER

1. How do you tend to deal with issues of confrontation? Do you tend to dive in and resolve it NOW or do you tend to avoid and procrastinate?

2. Which one of the ABCD's of anger is most difficult for you? Why is this one particularly difficult for you?

3. Chip said "From the book of Job and Psalms, God doesn't seem to get upset when people are honest and candid and even angry with Him to get to the bottom of issues. He can handle it." Has there ever been a time when you were angry at God?

4. Can you think of a time when you handled your anger appropriately and made it work for you? Share that experience with the group.

5. Read Matthew 5:23-26 NIV

   Therefore, if you are offering your gift at the altar and there remember that your brother has something against you, leave your gift there in front of the altar. First go and be reconciled to your brother; then come and offer your gift. "Settle matters quickly with your adversary who is taking you to court. Do it while you are still with him on the way, or he may hand you over to the judge, and the judge may hand you over to the officer, and you may be thrown into

prison. I tell you the truth, you will not get out until you have paid the last penny.

From this passage, what can we learn about resolving conflict?

_____

_____

6. Has there ever been a time when, no matter how much you tried, you couldn't resolve an issue or situation? What did you do? Looking back, would you do anything different?

_____

_____

7. Generally, dealing with anger "in person" is the best approach. Under what circumstances would it be more appropriate to handle an issue by phone or letter?

_____

_____

 LIVE IT OUT

If there is a conflict that you know needs to be addressed, make a commitment to take a step of action this week. Don't procrastinate.

*Additional Resource: **Invisible War** from Living on the Edge; 3x5 cards*

Session 6

GOD'S ANGER MANAGEMENT PLAN

THE FACTS:

The average man loses his temper about 6 times a week.

The average woman loses her temper about 3 times week.

Men tend to get mad about _____.

Women tend to get mad about _____.

All of us are twice as likely to express our anger at home more than at work or school

GOD'S 3-STEP PROCESS TO TAME THE WILD STALLION OF ANGER

My dear brothers, take note of this: Everyone should be quick to listen, slow to speak and slow to become angry, for man's anger does not bring about the righteous life that God desires.   JAMES 1:19-20 NIV

Step #1= "Be Quick to _____ *"*

- Our immediate response to God, others, circumstances, and our anger is to be "receptive listeners" not "reactionary responders."

- Key Question = What is this anger telling me?

Step #2= "Be Slow to _____"

When words are many, sin is not absent, but he who holds his tongue is wise.

PROVERBS 10:19 NIV

He who guards his lips guards his life, but he who speaks rashly will come to ruin.

PROVERBS 13:3 NIV

Do you see a man who speaks in haste? There is more hope for a fool than for him.

PROVERBS 29:20 NIV

- Our interim response to God, others, circumstances, and our anger is to "think before we speak."
- Key Question = What must I do to prevent a "verbal reflex response"?

Step #3= "Be Slow to _____"

Do not be quickly provoked in your spirit, for anger resides in the lap of fools.

ECCLESIASTES 7:9 NIV

- Our life changing response to anger begins when we replace "reaction" with "reflection."
- Key Question = What root issue (injustice, hurt, frustration, or insecurity) is behind this anger?

How can we deal with those painful root issues?

Diagnostic Question = What's behind my anger?

1. Am I Hurt?

- Tool = "I feel" messages

2. Am I Frustrated?

- Tool = "I desire" vs. "I demand" expectations

3. Am I Feeling Threatened?

- Tool = "Who's firing the darts? Is there something to learn? Whose approval do I need?"

🗩 TALK IT OVER

1. James gave us a very straightforward teaching about dealing with our anger. His 3-step strategy is:

   - Be quick to hear

   - Be slow to speak

   - Be slow to anger

   Which one of these 3 do you need to give attention to? What made you choose that one?

   _____

   _____

2. What could you do to be a better listener?

   _____

   _____

3. Proverbs 10:19 says, "When words are many, sin is not absent, but he who holds his tongue is wise." When are you most apt to speak when you shouldn't?

4. Words are incredibly powerful. Proverbs says that life and death is in the tongue. What is something life-giving that somebody said to you years ago that you still remember to this day?

5. What is something hurtful that somebody said to you years ago that you still remember to this day?

6. What are some practical tools that can help you guard your tongue and keep you from speaking rashly?

7. Self-awareness is critical when dealing with anger. When are you most easily provoked to anger?

 LIVE IT OUT

Take a 3x5 card this week and write out James 1:19-20. Work on memorizing these two verses this week.

Session 7

ELIMINATING STRESS BEFORE IT STARTS
PART 1

$AQ = (E + P) \times O426$

Anger Quotient = (Environment + Perspective) x Obedience to Ephesians 4:26

"Be angry, and yet do not sin; do not let the sun go down on your anger."

EPHESIANS 4:26 NASB

THE ENVIRONMENT

The Key is to Minimize Stress

1. Eliminate hurry –

    _____ and godliness are incompatible

    Hurry is often rooted in _____

2. Downsize expectations –

3. Learn to say no "kindly" –

4. Admit mistakes and imperfections –

5. Laugh more—don't take life or yourself so seriously –

    A cheerful heart is good medicine.

    PROVERBS 17:22 NIV

6. Take care of yourself –
    Get enough rest
    Eat good food
    Get adequate exercise

7. Know what triggers your anger –

*HALT - When you're **H**ungry, **A**ngry, **L**onely, or **T**ired, STOP*

 TALK IT OVER

1. What is one thing you can do to simplify your life and slow down?

2. Would you describe yourself as a hurrier? What are the by-product results to yourself and your relationships when you are always in a hurry?

3. What are the top 3 things that are causing stress in your life?

   Think back over your day today. When did you get stressed out today?

4. Where do you need to take the pressure off and downsize your expectations? What would your spouse or good friend say is an area where you need to downsize your expectations?

5. Where in your life do you need to say "no"? In order to reduce stress, what is one thing you could eliminate?

6. Do a little self-inventory for the last three months. How much laughter and fun has there been? What could you do this next week to "lighten up" and have some fun?

7. One way to reduce stress is to take care of ourselves. Which of the following do you need to work on?

    • Getting adequate rest

    • Eating healthy

    • Getting adequate exercise

    What is one action step you could take this week?

    _____

    _____

 LIVE IT OUT

Hold each other accountable for slowing down. Check in with each other this week to see how it's going.

Session 8

AQ = (E + P) x O426

Anger Quotient = (Environment + Perspective) x Obedience to Ephesians 4:26

Getting the Right Perspective (How do you look at life?)

MAXIMIZE YOUR RELATIONSHIP WITH GOD

1. Get right with God: believe in Him, confess your sins, forgive others.

Submit therefore to God. Resist the devil and he will flee from you. Draw near to God and He will draw near to you Cleanse your hands, you sinners; and purify your hearts, you double-minded.   JAMES 4:7-8 NASB

2. Experience God's unconditional love and acceptance.

The LORD your God is in your midst,
        the mighty one will save.
        He will rejoice over you with gladness,
        he will quiet you with his love,
        he will rejoice over you with singing.   ZEPHANIAH 3:17 NIV

3. Accept who God made you to be.

For You formed my inward parts;
        You wove me in my mother's womb.
I will give thanks to You, for I am fearfully and wonderfully made;
        Wonderful are Your works,
        And my soul knows it very well.

My frame was not hidden from You,
   When I was made in secret,
   And skillfully wrought in the depths of the earth;
Your eyes have seen my unformed substance;
   And in Your book were all written
   The days that were ordained for me,
   When as yet there was not one of them.

PSALM 139:13-16 NASB

4.   Trust God and His sovereignty—let Him be in control.

"To whom then will you liken Me
   That I would be his equal?" says the Holy One.
Lift up your eyes on high
   And see who has created these stars,
   The One who leads forth their host by number,
   He calls them all by name;
   Because of the greatness of His might and the strength of His power,
   Not one of them is missing.
Why do you say, O Jacob, and assert, O Israel,
   "My way is hidden from the LORD,
   And the justice due me escapes the notice of my God"?
Do you not know? Have you not heard?
   The Everlasting God, the LORD, the Creator of the ends of
   the earth does not become weary or tired

ISAIAH 40:25-28 NASB

5.   Be merciful.

But love your enemies, do good to them, and lend to them without expecting
to get anything back. Then your reward will be great, and you will be sons of
the Most High, because he is kind to the ungrateful and wicked. Be merciful,
just as your Father is merciful.

LUKE 6:35-36 NIV

6. Pray about everything.

Be anxious for nothing, but in everything by prayer and supplication with thanksgiving let your requests be made known to God. And the peace of God, which surpasses all comprehension, will guard your hearts and your minds in Christ Jesus.

PHILIPPIANS 4:6-7 NASB

TALK IT OVER

1. From the list of ways to Maximize Your Relationship with God, what is the one that you most need to apply?

2. Chip said, "The most miserable Christians in the world are those who are half-hearted in their relationship with God." How would you describe your walk with God over the last few months? Passionate? Lukewarm? Completely surrendered? Stuck?

3. God loves you too much to let you live in a way that is harmful and contrary to His plan. He will bring consequences into our life to help us get back on track. Describe a time in your life when you got away from God and what happened to bring you back.

4. When you were growing up, what was your view of God? How do you respond to the idea that God rejoices over you with gladness and singing?

5. What are some tools or practices that help you in your relationship with God?

6. When we really trust God's sovereignty, what are the practical outcomes in our lives?

7. At the close of this session, Chip challenged us to "Pray about Everything." What is going on in your world today that you need prayer for? Close your group time this week by praying for each other.

 **LIVE IT OUT**

This week read Isaiah 40. Then, write a letter to God expressing your trust in His sovereignty.

Session 9

HOW TO BE GOOD AND MAD
PART 1

Anger is a channel and God given emotion to maximize your potential in Christ.

Anger was designed by God to be a weapon, a tool, and a resource to help you respond in a powerful way to evil in the world.

Be angry, and yet do not sin; do not let the sun go down on your anger, and do not give the devil an opportunity. EPHESIANS 4:26-27 NASB

THE BOOK OF EPHESIANS

Chapters 1-3-What we believe (your worth in God's sight)

Chapters 4-6-How we behave (your walk in God's sight)

God's agenda for your life is to trust Him.

What's at stake – God gave you this gift of anger to transform your life to make you like Christ.

1. *God commands us to express our anger.*

- Ephesians 4:26a (NIV)

2. *God commands us to express our anger appropriately.*

- Ephesians 4: 26b (NIV)

3. One appropriate use of anger is righteous indignation.

- Jesus was visibly angry.
  Mark 3

- Jesus was verbally angry.
  Matthew 23

- Jesus was physically angry.
  Mark 11

 TALK IT OVER

1. What is going on in the world that is just "wrong" that makes you righteously mad (indignant)?

2. Is there an injustice going on around you that your group could address? Come up with one project that your group could take on.

   (Share with us on Facebook at Living on the Edge the project you are doing as a group.)

3. Read Mark 11:15-17. How is the picture of Jesus here different than how we typically see Jesus portrayed today?

4. What are some other biblical examples where we see Jesus/God expressing righteous anger?

5. When does "righteous indignation" become "unrighteous"? What would it look like to be angry at the right things but to express it in the wrong way?

_____

_____

6. What safeguards can help you express your anger yet do so appropriately?

_____

_____

Before you wrap up this session, spend a few minutes discussing what curriculum your group wants to do next.

 LIVE IT OUT

Do a little research this week on the area of injustice that your group identified. Have a conversation with a local expert, pick up a book, do a field trip, or get online to gather more information.

Session 10

HOW TO BE GOOD AND MAD
PART 2

HEALING THE WOUNDS OF ANGER

Step #1 – Cleanse the Wound

Get rid of all bitterness, rage and anger, brawling and slander, along with every form of malice.
EPHESIANS 4:31 NIV

HOW?

Confession and repentance of unresolved anger!

If you don't cleanse the wound, it will lead to infection.

Step #2 – Treat the Wound

Be kind and compassionate to one another, forgiving each other, just as in Christ God forgave you.
EPHESIANS 4:32 NIV

HOW?

Extend forgiveness and seek reconciliation!

As far as it depends on you!

Step #3 – Bandage the Wound

Be imitators of God, therefore, as dearly loved children ²and live a life of love, just as Christ loved us and gave himself up for us as a fragrant offering and sacrifice to God.
EPHESIANS 5:1-2 NIV

HOW?

Put the past behind you!

One of the most powerful tools in learning to forgive is _____ for the person that hurt you.

FORGIVE
Choice

 >

FORGIVING
Process

 >

Forgiven
Rejoice

 TALK IT OVER

1. Share an experience where you were wounded and have now worked through the process of forgiveness.

2. As you have worked through relational wounds, what helped you get past the hurt?

3. Read Psalm 51:1-13. What most strikes you about David's confession and repentance?

4. In Romans 12:18 NIV Paul said, "If it is possible, as far as it depends on you, live at peace with everyone." What advice would you give someone who was seeking reconciliation but has their efforts rejected by the other person?

5. What have you learned about "putting the past behind you"? How have you released past wounds and "let them go"?

6. In Luke 6:27-28 Jesus said, "But I tell you who hear me: Love your enemies, do good to those who hate you, bless those who curse you, pray for those who mistreat you." How could you do good (bless) someone that has hurt you? Get practical and specific.

7. Chip said that one of the most powerful tools for learning to forgive is praying for those who have hurt us. Spend some time as a group praying for each other and for those that may have hurt you in the past.

LIVE IT OUT

This week write out the top 3 lessons or skills you have learned from this series that you want to make sure stay with you. Then, share them with a friend and ask them to help you in this journey.

LEADER'S NOTES

Group Agreement

People come to groups with a variety of different expectations. The purpose of a group agreement is simply to make sure everyone is on the same page and that we have some common expectations. The following group agreement is a tool to help the group discuss specific guidelines together during your first meeting. Modify anything that does not work for your group, then be sure to discuss the questions on the next page. This will help you to have an even greater group experience!

WE AGREE TO THE FOLLOWING PRIORITIES

- Take the Bible Seriously — to seek to understand and apply God's truth in the Bible

- Group Attendance — to give priority to the group meeting
  (Call if I am going to be absent or late.)

- Safe Environment — to create a safe place where people can be heard and feel loved (no snap judgments or simple fixes)

- Be Confidential — to keep anything that is shared strictly confidential and within the group

- Spiritual Health — to give group members permission to help me live a godly, healthy spiritual life that is pleasing to God

- Building Relationships — to get to know the other members of the group and pray for them regularly

- Prayer — to regularly pray with and for each other

- Other

Our Game Plan

- Will we have refreshments?

- What will we do about childcare?

- What day and time will we meet?

- Where will we meet?

- How long will we meet each week?

How To Make This A Meaningful Experience For Your Group

BEFORE THE GROUP ARRIVES

1. **Be prepared.** Your personal preparation can make a huge difference in the quality of the group experience. We strongly suggest previewing both the DVD teaching program by Chip Ingram along with the accompanying parts of the study guide.

2. **Pray for your group members by name.** Ask God to use your time together to touch the heart of every person in your group. Expect God to challenge and change people as a result of this study.

3. **Provide refreshments.** There's nothing like food to help a group relax and connect with each other. For the first week, we suggest you prepare a snack, but after that, ask other group members to bring the food so that they share in the responsibilities of the group and make a commitment to return.

4. **Relax.** Don't try to imitate someone else's style of leading a group. Lead the group in a way that fits your style and temperament. Remember that people may feel a bit nervous showing up for a small group study, so put them at ease when they arrive. Make sure to have all the details covered prior to your group meeting, so that once people start arriving, you can focus on greeting them.

⌄ TAKE IT IN – WATCH THE VIDEO

1. **Arrange the room.** Set up the chairs in the room so that everyone can see the television. It's best to arrange the room in such a way that it is conducive to discussion.

2. **Get the video ready.** Each video session on the DVD has 3 components. During the first 2-3 minutes, Chip introduces this week's topic. Then, the group will watch the actual teaching content that Chip taught in front of a live audience. This portion of the video is roughly 25 minutes in length. Finally, Chip will then share some closing thoughts and set up the discussion topics for your group.

3. **Be sure to test your video equipment ahead of time.** Practice using the equipment and make sure you have located this week's lesson on the DVD menu. The video segments flow from one right into the next. So once you start the session, you won't have to stop the video until Chip has finished his closing thoughts and prepared the group for the first discussion question.

4. **Have enough materials on hand.** Before you start the video, make sure everyone has their own copy of the study guide. Encourage the group to open to this week's session and follow along with the teaching.

TALK IT OVER

Here are some guidelines for leading the discussion time:

1. **Make this a discussion, not a lecture.** Resist the temptation to do all the talking and to answer your own questions. Don't be afraid of a few moments of silence while people formulate their answers. And don't feel like you need to have all the answers. There is nothing wrong with simply responding "I don't know the answer to that, but I'll see if I can find an answer this week."

2. **Encourage everyone to participate.** Don't let one person dominate, but also don't pressure quieter members to speak during the first couple of sessions. After one person answers, don't immediately move on; ask what other people think, or say, "Would someone who hasn't shared like to add anything?"

3. **Affirm people's participation and input.** If an answer is clearly wrong, ask "What led you to that conclusion?" or ask what the rest of the group thinks. If a disagreement arises, don't be too quick to shut it down! The discussion can draw out important perspectives, and if you can't resolve it there, offer to research it further and return to the issue next week. However, if someone goes on the offensive and engages in personal attack of another person, you will need to step in as the leader. In the midst of spirited discussion, we must also remember that people are fragile and there is no place for disrespect.

4. **Detour when necessary.** If an important question is raised that is not in the study guide, take time to discuss it. Also, if someone shares something personal and emotional, take time for them. Stop and pray for them right then. Allow the Holy Spirit room to maneuver and follow His prompting when the discussion changes direction.

5. **Form subgroups.** One of the principles of small group life is "when numbers go up, sharing goes down." So, if you have a large group, you may want to split up into groups of 3-5 for discussion time. This is a great way to give everyone, even the quieter members, a chance to say something. Choose someone in the

group to guide each of the smaller groups through the discussion. This involves others in the leadership of the group and provides an opportunity for training new leaders.

6. **Pray.** Be sensitive to the fact that some people in your group may be uncomfortable praying out loud. As a general rule, don't call on people to pray unless you have asked them ahead of time or have heard them pray in public. But this can also be a time to help people build their confidence to pray in a group. Consider having prayer times that ask people to just say a word or sentence of thanks to God.

LIVE IT OUT

These simple suggestions will help you apply the lesson. Be sure and leave adequate time to talk about practical applications of the lesson. This is a great way to build group community.

Try these ideas together and hold each other accountable for completing them, then share how it went the following week.

A FINAL WORD...

Keep an eye on the clock. Be sensitive to time. Whatever is the agreed upon time commitment, try to stick with it. It is always better to finish the meeting with people wanting more rather than people walking away stressed out because the meeting went long.

Leader's Notes

Thanks for hosting this series on **Overcoming Emotions That Destroy**. Whether you are brand new at this or you are a seasoned veteran, God is going to use you. God has a long history of using ordinary people like us to get His work done.

These brief notes are intended to help prepare you for each week's session. By spending just a few minutes each week previewing the video and going over these leader's notes, you will set the table for a great group experience. Also, don't forget to pray for your group each week.

Session 1

- If your group doesn't know each other well, be sure that you spend some time getting acquainted. Don't rush right into the video lesson. Remember, small group is not just a study or a meeting, it is about relationships.

- Be sure to capture everyone's contact information. It is a good idea to send out an email with everybody's contact information so that the group can stay in touch.

- When you are ready to start the session, be sure that each person in your group has a copy of the study guide. The small group study guide is important for people to follow along and to take notes.

- The video lesson taught by Chip Ingram will be about 25 minutes in length. So, you will have plenty of time for discussion. Each session opens with Chip setting up the lesson. Then, the video will transition to his live teaching. And, at the end of the teaching, Chip will come back and wrap up the session as well as set up the first discussion question for the group.

- Several times Chip will ask you as the facilitator to lead the way by answering the first question.

- At the end of the study notes for each session is a section called Live It Out. This section has one idea or exercise that people in the group could do to deepen their experience with this teaching.

Session 2

- Why not begin your preparation by praying right now for the people in your group? You might even want to keep their names in your Bible. You may also want to ask people in your group how you can pray for them specifically.

- Also, if somebody doesn't come back this week, be sure and follow up with them. Even if you knew they were going to have to miss the group meeting, give them a call or shoot them an email letting them know that they were missed. It would also be appropriate to have a couple of other people in the group let them know they were missed.

- Each time your group meets take a few minutes to update on what has happened since the last group meeting. Ask people what they are learning and putting into practice. Remember, being a disciple of Jesus means becoming a "doer of the Word."

- During this week's session Chip is going to talk about Spewers, Stuffers, and Leakers. It will be a fun session of self-discovery and should generate a lot of great interaction.

- You will want to emphasize to the group the point that Chip made that none of these are better or worse than the others. Each of these faces of anger is simply about our wiring and personality.

- During Session 1 Chip emphasized the importance of confidentiality. The material covered during this series is delicate and sensitive. And, the discussion questions will likely lead to some very vulnerable discussions. So, emphasize again this week the issue of confidentiality. Nothing will cause the group to shut down more than feeling like the group isn't a safe place to share.

Session 3

ANGER IS A SECONDARY EMOTION • PART 1

- Did anybody miss last week's session? If so, make it a priority to follow up and let them know they were missed. It just might be your care for them that keeps them connected to the group.

- Share the load. One of the ways to raise the sense of ownership within the group is to get them involved in more than coming to the meeting. So, get someone to help with refreshments… find somebody else to be in charge of the prayer requests… get someone else to be in charge of any social gathering you plan… let someone else lead the discussion one night. Give away as much of the responsibility as possible. That is GOOD leadership.

- Think about last week's meeting for a moment. Was there anyone that didn't talk or participate? In every group there are extroverts and there are introverts. There are people who like to talk and then there are those who are quite content NOT to talk. Not everyone engages in the same way or at the same level but you do want to try and create an environment where everyone wants to participate.

- Follow-up questions. The only thing better than good questions are good follow- up questions. Questions are like onions. Each question allows another layer to be peeled back and get beneath the surface.

- Don't be afraid of silence. When you ask people a question, give them time to think about it. Don't feel like you have to fill every quiet moment with noise.

- At the end of the teaching session Chip will lead the group in prayer. And, during the closing, he will ask your group to bow their heads and close their eyes. Lead the way by bowing your head and taking his challenge seriously.

- Chip will ask those in your group to think about a situation where they have been hurt. Because of the nature of this topic, you will want to handle this carefully. Don't put anyone on the spot and let people share at whatever level they are comfortable.

Session 4

ANGER IS A SECONDARY EMOTION • PART 2

- As you get the group together this week, do a check-in from last week. Ask people how they felt as they left last week. Ask them if God has been speaking to them about the hurt they have been carrying around. And, finally, ask if anybody in the group made an effort to have a conversation about their hurt.

- Don't feel any pressure to get through all the questions. As people open up and talk, don't move on too quickly. Give them the space to consider what is going on inside them as they interact with this teaching.

- If your group is not sharing as much as you would like or if the discussion is being dominated by a person or two, try subgrouping. If your group is 8 people or more, this is a great way to up the level of participation.

  After watching the video tape, divide the group into a couple of smaller groups for the discussion time. It is good to get someone you think would be a good facilitator to agree to this ahead of time.

- As part of one of the discussion questions this week, you will be asked to read Ephesians 1:3-14. You will want to have your Bible out and if you have some extras, pass them out to the group so they can follow along with the passage.

- Encourage the group this week to do the Live It Out exercise. Your group will be asked to spend some time this week reflecting on what Chip said about the insecurities that we each struggle with. We are not very good at thinking about or talking about our insecurities. To help them think about this, the Live It Out exercise challenges the people in your group to write out thoughts, starting with this sentence "I feel most insecure when…."

Session 5

HOW TO MAKE YOUR ANGER WORK FOR YOU

- You are now at the halfway point of this series. How is it going? How well is the group connecting? Do a little assessment. What has been going well and what needs a little work?

- Chip is going to talk about the poison of unresolved conflict. One of the options Chip is going to share is writing a letter that helps you articulate what you are feeling. Most people will never need to mail their letter. However, someone may feel that they need to send the letter. If you have someone like that in your group, make sure that they understand that the motive is to be "redemptive."

- At the end of this week's session, Chip is going to encourage people to get a 3x5 card and write out the ABCD's of dealing with anger. It would be great if you had some cards at the group meeting that people could take home. Encourage them to write these out and review them several times this week.

- If someone shares an unresolved conflict that they are going through, be sure to pray for them and about the situation. Don't be afraid to do this right in the middle of the group meeting. You don't need to wait until the end of the group to pray. Do it right then, when the need and moment are fresh.

Session 6

GOD'S ANGER MANAGEMENT PLAN 39

- One way to deepen the level of community within your group is to spend time together outside the group meeting. If you have not already done so, plan something that will allow you to get to know each other better. Also, consider having someone else in the group take responsibility for your fellowship event.

- Confidentiality is crucial to group life. The moment trust is breached, people will shut down and close up. So, you may want to mention the importance of cofidentiality again this week just to keep it on people's radar.

- This week's session is about taming your temper. Chip will spend time unpacking James 1:19-20. Chip will also spend some time talking about the power of God's Word to transform us. This is a good week to remind people of the importance of a daily time with God.

- At the end of the session Chip will ask people again to take a 3x5 card. This time he will encourage them to write James 1:19-20 on the card. It would be helpful if you could have some 3x5 cards ready to hand out. Also, challenge the group not only to review these verses this coming week, but to work on memorizing this short passage.

Session 7

ELIMINATING STRESS BEFORE IT STARTS • PART 1

- Do a check-in at the beginning of your meeting to see if anyone has memorized James 1:19-20. If people didn't memorize this passage, challenge them again this week to give it a try.

- This week's session is a very practical teaching about reducing stress. There should be lots of lively discussion. So, you might want to leave a few extra minutes to make sure you can get through all the questions.

- Crucial to this session is follow up. Chip will challenge the group to consider what action steps they can take to slow down the pace of their lives. Encourage people to check in with each other this week to see how they are doing.

- Consider asking someone in your group to facilitate next week's lesson. Who knows, there might be a great potential small group leader in your group. It will give you a break and give them a chance to grow.

Session 8

ELIMINATING STRESS BEFORE IT STARTS • PART 2

- Follow up from last week's session and find out how people did with trying to slow down a bit. Encourage people to take this challenge seriously and to keep working on it.

- At the beginning of this session, Chip will talk about the importance of putting your faith in Christ. If there is someone in your group who isn't a believer, this would be a good session to talk about faith in Christ. You might say something like, "The first step to becoming emotionally healthy is to have a personal relationship with Christ. If you have questions about whether or not you are a Christian, I would be happy to talk with you after our group meeting."

- One of the questions this week asks people to describe a time in their life when they got away from God and what happened to bring them back. This can be a little intimidating for people to share. As the facilitator, it might be helpful for you to think about this question ahead of time and lead out in answering that question.

- During this session Chip shares some of the tools he uses to help him with his walk with God (an ipod with worship music, a journal, book of Scriptures on prayer). If you have a tool or two that you use in your walk with God, it would be good for you to bring that tool to the group meeting and share how you use it.

Session 9

- Since this is the next to the last week of this study, you might want to spend some time this week talking about what your group is going to do after you complete this study.

- As this series winds down, this is a good time to plan some kind of party or fellowship after you complete the study. Find the "party person" in your group and ask them to take on the responsibility of planning a fun experience for the group. Also, use this party as a time for people to share how God has used this series to grow them and change them.

- During this week's session Chip is going to talk about times when it is good and appropriate to get angry. He will close the session with a challenge for your group to consider an injustice that you could address. Spend some time talking about how your group could mobilize to make a difference. If you decide on a project, please share with us on Facebook at Living on the Edge what you are doing as a group.

Session 10

- Since this is your last session in this series, make sure that you have talked about what your group is going to do next. Also, consider taking a week or two break and doing a party/fellowship together.

- In this session Chip is going to talk about how we deal with our relational wounds. This session has the potential for the discussion to be very personal and transparent. So, this might be a good time to subgroup for the discussion. People will often open up more when there is a smaller group.

- During one of the discussion questions, the group will be asked to spend some time reading and talking about Psalm 51:1-13. Be sure to have a couple of Bibles available for the group to use.

- This week's Live It Out challenge is… write out the top 3 lessons or skills you have learned from this series that you want to make sure stay with you. Then, share them with a friend and ask them to help you in this journey. You might encourage people in the group to email each other their top 3 lessons or skills that they are taking away from this series.

Prayer and Praise

One of the most important things you can do in your group is to pray with and for each other. Write down each other's concerns here so you can remember to pray for these requests during the week!

Use the Follow Up box to record an answer to a prayer or to write down how you might want to follow up with the person making the request. This could be a phone call, an email, or a card. Your personal concern will mean a lot!

PERSON	PRAYER REQUEST	FOLLOW UP

PERSON	PRAYER REQUEST	FOLLOW UP

PERSON	PRAYER REQUEST	FOLLOW UP

PERSON	PRAYER REQUEST	FOLLOW UP

PERSON	PRAYER REQUEST	FOLLOW UP

PERSON	PRAYER REQUEST	FOLLOW UP

Group Roster

NAME	HOME PHONE	EMAIL

Group Roster

NAME	HOME PHONE	EMAIL

What's Next?
More Group Studies from Chip Ingram:

Balancing Life's Demands
Biblical Priorities for a Busy Life
Busy, tired and stressed out? Learn how to put "first things first" and find peace in the midst of pressure and adversity.

Culture Shock
A Biblical Response to Today's Most Divisive Issues
Bring light—not heat—to divisive issues, such as abortion, homosexuality, sex, politics, the environment, politics and more.

Doing Good
What Happens When Christians Really Live Like Christians
This series clarifies what Doing Good will do in you and then through you, for the benefit of others and the glory of God.

Experiencing God's Dream for Your Marriage
Practical Tools for a Thriving Marriage
Examine God's design for marriage and the real life tools and practices that will transform it for a lifetime.

Five Lies that Ruin Relationships
Building Truth-Based Relationships
Uncover five powerful lies that wreck relationships and experience the freedom of understanding how to recognize God's truth.

The Genius of Generosity
Lessons from a Secret Pact Between Friends
The smartest financial move you can make is to invest in God's Kingdom. Learn His design for wise giving and generous living.

The Real God
How He Longs for You to See Him
A deeper look at seven attributes of God's character that will change the way you think, pray and live.

Good to Great in God's Eyes
10 Practices Great Christians Have in Common
If you long for spiritual breakthrough, take a closer look at ten powerful practices that will rekindle a fresh infusion of faith.

The Real Heaven
It's Not What You Think
Chip Ingram digs into scripture to reveal what heaven will be like, what we'll do there, and how we're to prepare for eternity today.

Holy Ambition
Turning God-Shaped Dreams Into Reality
Do you long to turn a God-inspired dream into reality? Learn how God uses everyday believers to accomplish extraordinary things.

House or Home: Marriage Edition
God's Blueprint for a Great Marriage
Get back to the blueprint and examine God's plan for marriages that last for a lifetime.

House or Home: Parenting Edition
God's Blueprint for Biblical Parenting
Timeless truths about God's blueprint for parenting, and the potential to forever change the trajectory of your family.

What's Next?

More Group Studies from Chip Ingram:

The Invisible War
The Believer's Guide to Satan, Demons and Spiritual Warfare
Learn how to clothe yourself with God's "spiritual armor" and be confident of victory over the enemy of your soul.

Love, Sex and Lasting Relationships   **UPDATED**
God's Prescription to Enhance Your Love Life
Do you believe in "true love"? Discover a better way to find love, stay in love, and build intimacy that lasts a lifetime.

Overcoming Emotions that Destroy
Constructive Tools for Destructive Emotions
We all struggle with destructive emotions that can ruin relationships. Learn God's plan to overcome angry feelings for good.

Spiritual Simplicity
Doing Less · Loving More
If you crave simplicity and yearn for peace this study is for you. Spiritual simplicity can only occur when we do less and love more.

Transformed
The Miracle of Life Change
Ready to make a change? Explore God's process of true transformation and learn to spot barriers that hold you back from receiving God's best.

True Spirituality
Becoming a Romans 12 Christian
We live in a world that is activity-heavy and relationship-light. Learn the next steps toward True Spirituality.

Why I Believe
Answers to Life's Most Difficult Questions
Can miracles be explained? Is there really a God? There are solid, logical answers about claims of the Christian faith.

Your Divine Design
Discover, Develop and Deploy Your Spiritual Gifts
How has God uniquely wired you? Discover God's purpose for spiritual gifts and how to identify your own.

Download the Chip Ingram App

The Chip Ingram App delivers daily devotionals, broadcasts, message notes, blog articles and more right on your mobile device.